Theory Time!

Step by Step Instructions for ABRSM and Other Exams

Grade 3

by

DAVID TURNBULL

CONTENTS

Bosworth

5.95

THEORY TIME!

Grade 3

The purpose of these books is to teach the principles of music theory. They are intended not only for pupils who want to pass theory examinations, but also for all those who would like to learn something about the theory of music as part of their general education. This book covers the syllabus of Grade 3 of the Associated Board.

The sections of the book explain the ideas you need to know, and test your understanding with frequent questions. Write down the answers to these questions in the spaces provided, and then look up the printed answers.

You will notice that answers to questions are always printed on different pages from the questions themselves. The answers to Page 1 questions are in the margin of Page 2, for example. Make sure that you look up the printed answers *only* after you have written down your own, if you want to make good progress.

You can use this book with your teacher, who can set you pages to work through and then explain any difficulties you may have. Or you can use it to teach yourself, and you can use it for revision.

The sections of the book deal with different aspects of theory, but you need not work through to the end of each section before going on to the next. Your teacher may wish to recommend a different order of working — for example part of Section 1, then part of Section 2 before returning to complete Section 1. However, it is recommended that you should finish this book before you go on to Grade 4.

Extra practice can be got from past examination papers for the grade, published every year by the Associated Board of the Royal Schools of Music, and from *Music Theory in Practice – Grade 3* by Eric Taylor, also published by the Associated Board.

David Turnbull
Solihull, England, 1994

THEORY TIME! GRADE 3

Section 1 – Time

Answers to questions on this page are in the margin of Page 2

demisemi-quaver notes

1 In Grade 3, demisemiquaver notes and rests must be known, as well as the notes used in Grades 1 and 2.

The **demisemiquaver** has three tails. The American term for a demisemiquaver is a *thirty-second note,* because thirty-two demisemiquavers are equal in length to one semibreve.

Two demisemiquavers equal the length of one semiquaver.

How many demisemiquavers equal (a) a crotchet? __8__ (b) a minim? __16__

2 Demisemiquavers may be beamed together up to the value of a beat. As demisemiquavers have three tails, there are three beams.

Rewrite, beaming demisemiquavers:

(Some music printers print beams with the outer beam continuous but the inner beams split for greater clarity, as shown above right.)

demisemi-quaver rests

3 Demisemiquaver rests, like demisemiquavers, have three tails.

Insert rests at * to complete these bars:

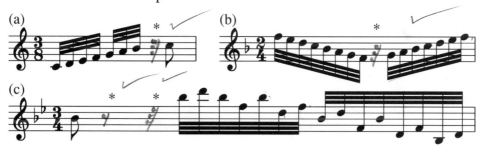

simple times **4** In Grade 1, times set were $\frac{2}{4}$, $\frac{3}{4}$ and $\frac{4}{4}$, all with crotchet beats. In Grade 2, times set were $\frac{2}{2}$, $\frac{3}{2}$ and $\frac{4}{2}$ with minim beats, and $\frac{3}{8}$ time with quaver beats.

All these are called **simple** times, because beats in each case can be divided into **two** smaller equal notes, as in these examples:

Answers to Page 2 questions

TEST 1

1 (a) $\frac{3}{8}$ (b) $\frac{4}{4}$ or **C**

(c) $\frac{2}{4}$ (d) $\frac{3}{2}$

2

3

5 duple

**TEST 1
revision of
simple times**

1 Write in the missing time signatures:

(a) (b)

(c)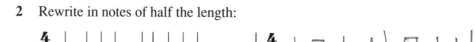

2 Rewrite in notes of half the length:

3 Pencil beats over bars, and insert any missing bar lines:

(a) 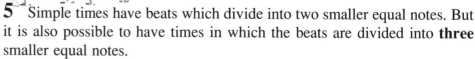 (b)

*If you have made more than two mistakes, read over Section 1 in Theory Time!
Grade 2.*

1 (a) 8 (b) 16

2 (a)

(b)

3 (a)

(b)   (c)

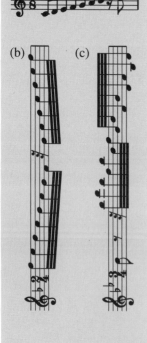

**compound
times**

5 Simple times have beats which divide into two smaller equal notes. But it is also possible to have times in which the beats are divided into **three** smaller equal notes.

Times in which the beats divide into three smaller equal notes are called **compound** times.

**dotted
crotchet
beats**

The two dotted crotchet beats below cannot be easily divided into two smaller notes, but they *can* be easily divided into three quavers:

What do we call any time which has two beats in a bar? Duple

**compound
duple time**

6 Each beat in the bar in **5** above can be divided into three, so the time is a **compound** time.

There are two beats in the bar, so the time is **duple**.

The bar in **5** is therefore in **compound duple** time.

We must find a time signature for the bar.

In time signatures of simple times, like $\frac{2}{4}$, the bottom number shows us what type of note is used as the beat. If **4** is the bottom figure, the beat is a crotchet, because four crotchets equal the length of a semibreve.

7 In the compound duple bar in **5**, however, the beats are *dotted* crotchets, and no whole number of dotted crotchets equals a semibreve.

(handwritten top margin)
6 ← six beats = 6 quaver beats in a bar.
8 ← quaver beats
↓
count 2
♩. ♩.
1   2

**Answers to
Page 4 questions**

We will therefore have to use the notes which are the *divisions* of the beats to give a bottom number for the time signature. Here are the main beats and their quaver divisions again:

Eight quavers are equal in length to a semibreve, so the bottom number of our time signature is **8**.

How many quavers are there in the bar above? __6__

⁶⁄₈ time

8 The time signature of our compound duple time bar is therefore ⁶⁄₈. How many beats are there in a bar of ⁶⁄₈ time, six or two? __2__

9 ⁶⁄₈ time is compound duple time with two dotted crotchet beats. Each beat can be divided into three quavers.

Notes which have tails must be beamed together up to the value of a dotted crotchet beat.

Pencil above this bar the two dotted crotchet beats and put in the beat divisions. Then rewrite it with the notes correctly grouped.

compound triple time

10 Here is a bar containing three dotted crotchet beats.

As there are three beats the time is a triple time. As the beats divide into three, the time is **compound triple**.

(a) What is its time signature? __⁹⁄₈__

⁹⁄₈ time

Compound triple time with dotted crotchet beats is ⁹⁄₈ time.

(b) Rewrite this bar with notes correctly grouped. Pencil in above the bar main beats, and beat divisions.

11 Here is a bar containing four dotted crotchet beats.

(a) What is the name of this time? __Compound Quadruple__

(b) What is its time signature? __¹²⁄₈__

TEST 2

(a) ⁶⁄₈ compound duple

(b) ¹²⁄₈ compound quadruple

(c) ⁹⁄₈ compound triple

(d) ⁶⁄₈ compound duple

**compound
quadruple
time 12/8**

12 Compound quadruple time with dotted crotchet beats is 12/8 time.

7 six

**TEST 2
compound
times**

Write in the time signature of each of these bars, and underneath the bar write the name of the time:

(a) *time name* Compound Duple

8 two

(b) *time name* Compound Quadruple

(c) *time name* Compound Triple   (d) *time name* Compound Duple

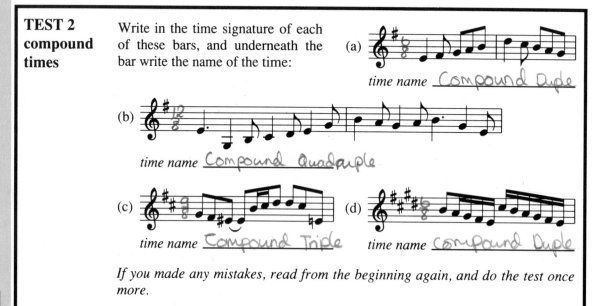

If you made any mistakes, read from the beginning again, and do the test once more.

9

**grouping of
notes in 6/8, 9/8
and 12/8**

13 For now, in 6/8, 9/8 and 12/8 times always work in dotted crotchet groups. However, you may see the following longer notes:

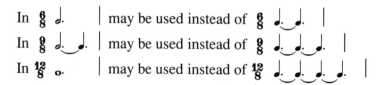

In 6/8 𝅗𝅥. | may be used instead of 6/8 𝅘𝅥.‿𝅘𝅥. |

In 9/8 𝅗𝅥.‿𝅗𝅥. | may be used instead of 9/8 𝅘𝅥.‿𝅘𝅥.‿𝅘𝅥. |

In 12/8 𝅝. | may be used instead of 12/8 𝅘𝅥.‿𝅘𝅥.‿𝅘𝅥.‿𝅘𝅥. |

10 (a) 9/8

**rests in 6/8, 9/8
and 12/8 times**

14 Use dotted crotchet rests for beats in your own work, but be prepared to see 𝄽 𝄾 written instead of 𝄽. sometimes.

If a rest is required which is *less* than a dotted crotchet beat in length,

- divide the dotted crotchet beat into its three quaver subdivisions,
- complete each quaver subdivision in turn with a rest.

In this example, there is only a semiquaver present of the first beat. The first quaver subdivision is completed with a semiquaver rest, and the remainder of the beat with two quaver rests.

(b)

(A crotchet rest can be used instead of the *first two* quaver rests of a beat, but separate quaver rests must be used for the last two, as here — 𝄽 𝄾 is allowed, but not 𝄾 𝄽).

11 (a) compound
           quadruple time

     (b) 12/8

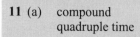

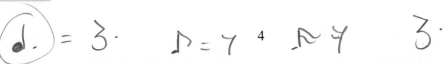

4

whole-bar rests

15 Whole-bar rests in these times are always shown by *semibreve* rests.

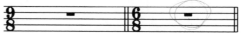

completion of bars with notes or rests

16 You may need to complete bars by inserting notes or rests. Look at this example:

The time signature, **12/8** , tells you that there should be four dotted crotchet beats in the bar. The beats have been put over the top of the bar, and the beat divisions pencilled in.

(a) Which beat is incomplete? ___2___

(b) What single note or rest would complete the bar? ___quaver___

(c) Write it in.

**TEST 3
compound
times**

1 Complete the following by adding single notes at *. Pencil in beats and beat divisions in all questions.

(a) 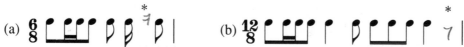 (b)

(c)

2 Complete the following by adding rests at *.

*If you made more than two mistakes, read **5–16** again and do the test once more.*

---

17 Compare these two bars:

The first is in a simple duple time, **2/4**. The second is in a compound duple time, **6/8**. However, both bars will *sound* the same if the beats are played at the same tempo.

Rewrite this **9/8** bar in **3/4** time so that the sound is unaltered:

19 (a) 2

(b) dotted crotchet

(c) No

(d) bars 1 and 2, and 3 and 4

(e) compound

(f) **9/8**

(g) between 2 and 3

finding the time of bars

18 You will often have to decide if music is in a simple time, or a compound time. Here are some hints to help you.

1 Simple times —

- If quavers and semiquavers are grouped in twos or fours, the time is likely to be a simple time.
- If triplets are used, the time is likely to be a simple time.

2 Compound times —

- If quavers are grouped in threes, the time is likely to be a compound time, (or $\frac{3}{8}$ – *see below*).
- If dotted crotchet rests are used, the time is likely to be a compound time, (or $\frac{3}{8}$ – *see below*).

$\frac{3}{8}$ **time** is sometimes difficult to recognise. It is a simple time, which may contain triplets, but it has quavers grouped in threes and dotted crotchet rests. If a passage looks at first as if it is in a compound time, but then proves not to be in $\frac{6}{8}$, $\frac{9}{8}$ or $\frac{12}{8}$, see if it is in $\frac{3}{8}$ time.

16 (a) beat 2

(b) a quaver

(c)

TEST 3 Answers

1 (a)

(b)

(c)

2

17

insertion of barlines

19 If you need to insert missing barlines, work as shown below.

A. When the time signature is given.

(a) How many beats should there be in a bar? _2_ ✓

(b) What type of note is used as the beat? _quaver_ ✓

Now pencil in beats and beat divisions.

(c) Count beats to where the first bar should end. Is there a barline in place? _NO_ If not, insert it. Continue in the same way to the end.

(d) Between which bars did you need to insert barlines? _____

B. When the time signature is not given. This is more difficult, and often requires some trial and error. Look at the passage below:

(e) Read over the hints in **18**. Is this music likely to be in simple or in compound time? _Compound_ ✓

(f) Try each of the times $\frac{6}{8}$, $\frac{9}{8}$ and $\frac{12}{8}$ in turn. Which is correct? _$\frac{9}{8}$_ ✓

(g) Between which bars did you need to put a barline? _2 + 3_ ✓

20 So far, all rhythms and melodies have started on the first beat of the first bar. But many rhythms and melodies start before the first full bar, like this:

If a rhythm or a melody starts before the first beat of the first bar, it is said to start on an 'up-beat' or **anacrusis.** Work out the time from the first *complete* bar. The anacrusis is discussed further in section 5.

In what time is the example above? $\frac{2}{4}$

TEST 4 simple and compound time signatures

1 Insert the time signatures and name the times in the following, which all start on the first beats of bars.

(a)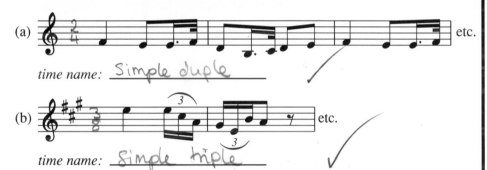

time name: Simple duple

(b)

time name: Simple triple

(c)

time name: Compound duple

(d)

time name: Compound Quadruple.

(e)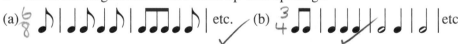

time name: Compound triple.

2 Insert time signatures before these up-beat openings:

*If you made more than one mistake, read **17–20** again and do the test once more.*

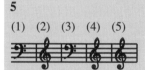

Answers to questions on this page are in the margin of Page 7

1 For Grade 3, you need to know notes in the treble and bass clefs, including those on any number of ledger lines.

Here is a revision test of Grades 1 and 2 notes:

**TEST 5
revision of
treble and
bass clef**

1 Name the treble clef notes below:

1 C 2 A 3 C♯ 4 D 5 A 6 G 7 B♭ 8 B♭ 9 F♯ 10 C

2 Name the bass clef notes below:

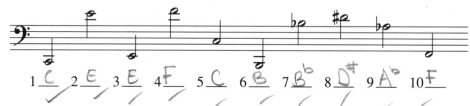

1 C 2 E 3 E 4 F 5 C 6 B 7 B♭ 8 D♯ 9 A♭ 10 F

3 Rewrite in the bass clef but at the same pitch:

4 Rewrite in the treble clef but at the same pitch:

5 Write in the correct clefs to make these the notes named here:

(1) middle C   (2)   B   (3)   F   (4)   A   (5) middle C

If you made more than 2 mistakes, work through pages 9–11 of **Theory Time!**
Grade 2, *then do the test again.*

TEST 4 Answers

1 (a) 2/4
simple duple

(b) 3/8
simple triple

(c) 6/8
compound duple

(d) 12/8
compound
quadruple

(e) 9/8
compound triple

2 (a) 6/8   (b) 3/4

**more about
ledger lines**

2 There is no limit to the number of ledger lines which can be used, but more than four are uncommon.

**ledger lines
above the
treble clef**

Here are the notes from F at the top of the treble clef on ledger lines:

F A C E G B

Here are the notes in the spaces between the ledger lines above the treble clef – remember the sentence '**G**reat **B**ig **D**ogs **F**rom **A**frica'.

G B D F A C

ledger lines below the treble clef

3 Here are notes on ledger lines below the treble clef, followed by the notes in the spaces between the ledger lines:

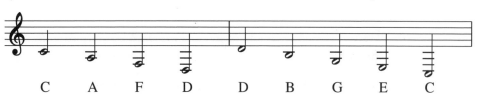

C   A   F   D   D   B   G   E   C

ledger lines above the bass clef

4 The top line of the bass clef carries the note A. Here are the notes on the ledger lines above the bass clef, followed by the notes in the spaces:

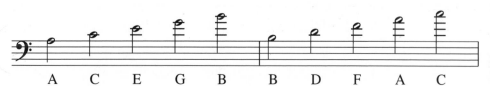

A   C   E   G   B   B   D   F   A   C

ledger lines below the bass clef

5 The bottom line of the bass clef carries the note G. Here are the notes on ledger lines below the bass clef, followed by the notes in the spaces:

G   E   C   A   F   F   D   B   G   E

When naming ledger line notes, always work from the top or bottom line of the stave, checking carefully that you haven't missed out any letters of the alphabet.

TEST 6 ledger line notes

1 Name these notes:

1 A   2 A   3 E   4 F   5 D   6 G   7 E   8 C#   9 B   10 Bb

2 Name these notes:

1 C   2 C#   3 F#   4 B   5 B   6 A   7 D   8 Db   9 F   10 B

3 Rewrite in the treble clef but at the same pitch. The first note is given.

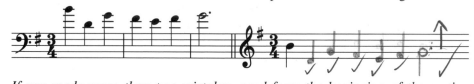

If you made more than two mistakes, read from the beginning of the section again and do the test once more.

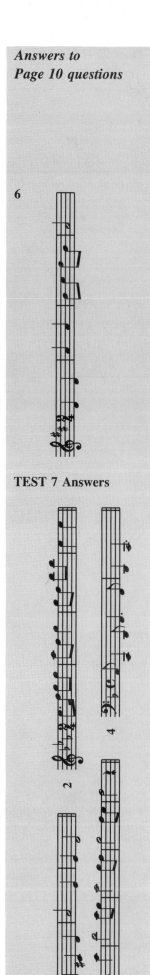

6

TEST 7 Answers

2

4

1

3

transposing **6** To transpose something means to move it from one place to another. Music may be transposed. Look at the melody below:

In 1(a), note 1 is middle C. Note 2 is D above middle C. Note 3 is E above middle C. Note 4 is B below middle C, and note 5 is middle C.

In 1(b), all the notes have been moved up an octave. Note 1 is C an octave above middle C. Note 2 is D an octave above note 2 of (a), and so on. The melody 1(b) has been **transposed up** an octave from 1(a).

We can also transpose the music down an octave. This time we will use the bass clef for the transposed version, so that we don't have to use too many ledger lines:

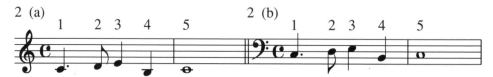

In 2(a), note 1 is middle C. In 2(b), note 1 is the C an octave *below* middle C. Notes 2 to 5 are all an octave below notes 2 to 5 in 2(a).

Transpose this melody an octave higher, writing it in the treble clef. Don't forget to put in the clef, key and time signatures.

TEST 6 Answers

1 (1) A
   (2) A
   (3) E
   (4) F
   (5) D
   (6) G
   (7) E
   (8) C sharp
   (9) B
  (10) B flat

2 (1) C
   (2) C sharp
   (3) F sharp
   (4) B
   (5) G
   (6) A
   (7) D
   (8) D flat
   (9) F
  (10) G

3

TEST 7
transposing
by an octave

1 Transpose this melody up an octave and write it in the treble clef:

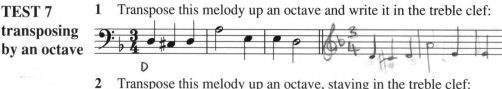

2 Transpose this melody up an octave, staying in the treble clef:

3 Transpose this melody down an octave and write it in the bass clef:

4 Transpose this melody down an octave, staying in the bass clef:

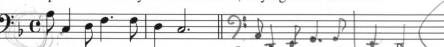

If you made any mistakes, read over 6 again and do the test once more.

Section 3 – Scales & Keys

grade 3 scales

1 In Grade 3, major and minor scales with key signatures up to and including four sharps and four flats must be known. You must know both the melodic and harmonic forms of the minor scale.

major scales – revision

2 All major scales have the same intervals between the degrees of the scale. Look at C major:

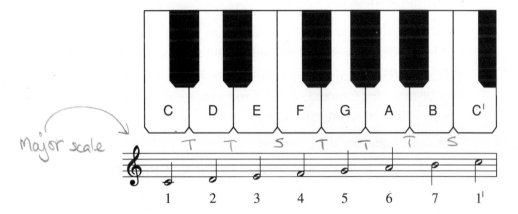

Between the first and second degrees there is an interval of a **tone**;
Between the second and third degrees there is an interval of a **tone**;
Between the third and fourth degrees there is an interval of a **semitone**.

Between the fourth and fifth degrees, the fifth and sixth degrees and the sixth and seventh degrees there are **tones**.

Between the seventh degree and the top keynote there is a **semitone**.

3 In C major, the Tone–Tone–Semitone–Tone–Tone–Tone–Semitone order of intervals can be kept by using white notes only. In all other major scales, one or more black notes must be used.

scales with sharps

4 There are two series of major scales, one using sharps, and the other using flats.

Look at the key signatures of scales in the sharp series we have already learnt for Grades 1 and 2.

C major has no sharps or flats.

The fifth degree of C major is G. The major scale starting on G requires **one** sharp – F sharp, for its seventh degree.

The fifth degree of G is D. D major scale requires **two** sharps – the F sharp of G major, and a sharp for its own seventh degree, C sharp.

The fifth degree of D is A. A major scale requires **three** sharps – the F sharp and C sharp of D major, and a sharp for its own seventh degree, G sharp.

Answers to Page 12 questions

4 (a) E

  (b) 4

  (c) D sharp

5 (a) a semitone

  (b) a semitone

(a) What note is the fifth degree of A? *E* ✓ C, G, D, A.

(b) How many sharps will the scale starting on that note require? *4* ✓

(c) What is the name of that scale's seventh degree? *D#* ✓

E major scale

5 E major scale has therefore four sharps. They are **F** sharp, **C** sharp, **G** sharp and **D** sharp.

Notice that the sharps above are listed in the order in which they enter the table of keys with sharps, and not in alphabetical order.

order of entry of sharps

There are seven major scales with sharps. Though you need to know only four of them for Grade 3, it is a good idea to learn now the order in which sharps enter the complete series.

You can remember it by the sentence

Father Charles Goes Down And Ends Battle

intervals in E major

Look at the diagram of the keyboard, and the notes of E major scale on the stave:

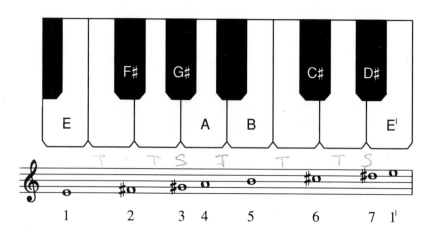

Between E (1) and F sharp (2) there is a **tone**. Between F sharp (2) and G sharp (3) there is a **tone**.

(a) What is the interval between G sharp (3) and A (4)? *Semitone* ✓

Between A (4) and B (5) there is a **tone**. Between B (5) and C sharp (6) there is a **tone**. Between C sharp (6) and D sharp (7) there is a **tone**.

(b) What is the interval between D sharp (7) and top E? *Semitone* ✓

The T-T-S T T-T-S relationship of intervals of a major scale is kept in E major.

E major key signature

6 Notice that the key signature of E major is written using the G sharp at the *top* of the stave in both treble and bass clefs:

12

Write out the table of key signatures of major keys with sharps up to and including E major. After each key signature write in the first note of the major scale (called the **tonic**) as a semibreve. C major is done for you.

major scales with flats

7 Look at the key signatures of scales in the flat series we have learned in Grades 1 and 2.

C major has no sharps or flats.

The fourth degree of C major is F. The major scale starting on F requires **one** flat – B flat, for its fourth degree.

The fourth degree of F major is B flat. B flat major scale requires **two** flats – the B flat of F major, and a flat for its own fourth degree, E flat.

The fourth degree of B flat major is E flat. E flat major scale requires **three** flats – the B flat and E flat of B flat major, and a flat for its own fourth degree.

(a) What note is the fourth degree of E flat major? _A♭_

(b) How many flats will the scale starting on that note need? _4_

(c) What is the name of that new scale's fourth degree? _D♭_

8 (b) a semitone

10

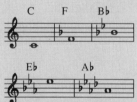

A♭ major scale

8 **A flat major** scale has therefore four flats. They are **B** flat, **E** flat, **A** flat and **D** flat. Notice that the flats above are listed in the order in which they enter the table of keys with flats, and *not* in alphabetical order.

There are seven scales with flats altogether. Though you need to know only four of them for Grade 3, it is sensible to learn now the order in which flats enter the complete series.

(a) What sentence gives you the order in which *sharps* enter?

11 (a) flats

(b) Yes

(c) Yes

(d) No

order of entry of flats

If you reverse the words of the sentence you get another:

Battle Ends And Down Goes Charles' Father.

This shows you the order in which flats enter the series.

(e) B flat major

13

6

7 (a) A flat

(b) four

(c) D flat

8 (a)
Father Charles Goes
Down And Ends Battle

intervals in A♭ major scale

Look at the diagram of the keyboard, and the notes of A flat major scale on the stave:

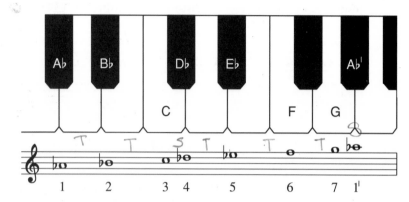

Between A flat (1) and B flat (2) there is a **tone**. Between B flat (2) and C (3) there is a **tone**. Between C (3) and D flat (4) there is a **semitone**.

Between D flat (4) and E flat (5) there is a **tone**. Between E flat (5) and F (6) there is a **tone**. Between F (6) and G (7) there is a **tone**.

(b) What interval is there between G (7) and the top A flat? *Semitone*

key signature of A♭ major

9 The key signature of A flat major is written with flats being entered in the order B, E, A, D:

table of major keys with flats

10 Write out the table of key signatures of keys with up to four flats. After each key signature write in the first note of the scale (the **tonic**) as a semibreve. C major has been done for you.

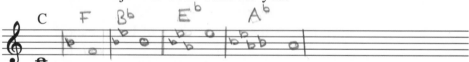

finding the key of a passage

11 Use these tables to help you find the key of passages where no key signature is given.

Suppose you wish to decide the key of this melody. Work as follows:

(a) Does it include sharps, or flats? *Flats.*

(b) Is the first flat of the series, B flat, present? *Yes* ✓

(c) Is the second flat of the series, E flat, present? *Yes* ✓

(d) Is the third flat of the series, A flat, present? *No* ✓

The first two flats only of the series are present. Look at your table of keys with flats.

(e) Which major key contains two flats? *B♭* ✓

Use the same method when deciding the names of keys with sharps.

14

Tonic = First degree.

**TEST 8
major key
signatures**

1 Write out the series of key signatures with sharps, inserting tonics:

2 Write out the series of key signatures with flats, inserting tonics:

3 Name the keys of the following phrases:

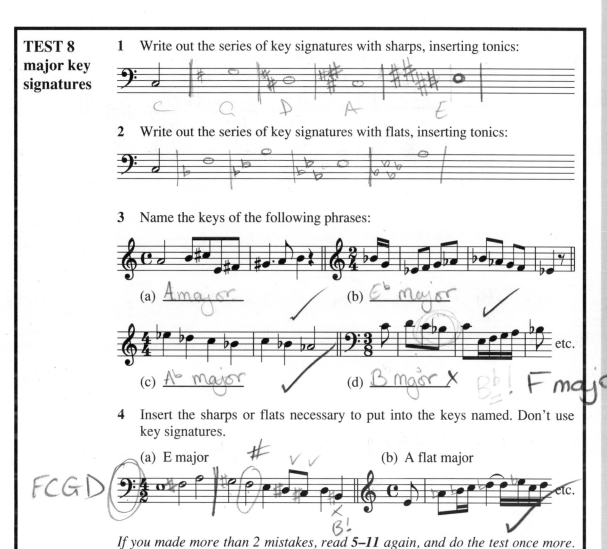

(a) A major   (b) E♭ major

(c) A♭ major   (d) B major ✗   B♭! F major B♭ has B♭E♭   B♭E♭A♭ = E♭ major!

4 Insert the sharps or flats necessary to put into the keys named. Don't use key signatures.

(a) E major   (b) A flat major

FCGD

If you made more than 2 mistakes, read 5–11 again, and do the test once more.

14 C major

15 the sixth

16 (a) E

(b) E minor

(c) D

(d) D minor

17 (a)

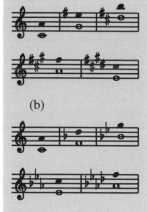

(b)

minor scales 12 In Grade 2, the scales of A minor, E minor and D minor were set for study. In Grade 3, the minor scales of B, F♯, C♯, G, C and F are added.

There are two types of minor scales in use now, called **melodic** minors and **harmonic** minors. Both types have to be known for Grade 3.

These scales are descended from an older form of minor scale, the *natural minor scale,* which we will study first.

**A natural
minor**

13 The white notes on the keyboard from A to A¹ are the notes of A natural minor.

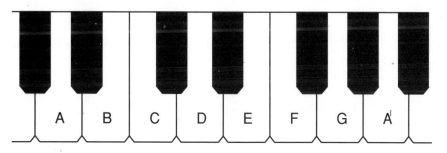

The intervals between the notes are **Tone – Semitone – Tone – Tone – Semitone – Tone – Tone**, or T-S-T T-S-T T for short.

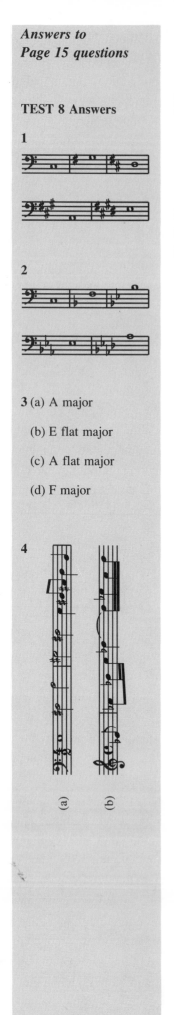

TEST 8 Answers

1

2

3 (a) A major

(b) E flat major

(c) A flat major

(d) F major

4

(a)   (b)

14   The key signature of any type of minor scale – natural minor, melodic minor or harmonic minor – is always taken from the notes of the natural minor scale. The key signature of A minor has no sharps or flats.

What *major* scale has the same key signature as A minor? _C major_ ✓

up a relative minor.

relative majors and minors

15   Because C major has the same key signature as A minor, we call C major the **relative major** of A minor. A minor is likewise the **relative minor** of C major.

What degree is A in the key of C major? _6_ ✓

16   The tonic of the relative minor is always the **sixth degree** of the major scale.

We can adapt our tables of key signatures to show both major keys and minors. Here is how both tables will start:

'sharp' key table

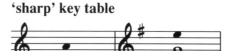

'flat' key table

C major and A minor have the same key signature. The tonic of C is shown as a semibreve on the chart. The tonic of A minor, the sixth note of C major, is shown as a crotchet head.

(a) What note is the sixth note of G major? _E_ ✓

(b) What scale is therefore the relative minor of G major? _E minor._ ✓

(c) What note is the sixth note of F major? _D_ ✓

(d) What scale is therefore the relative minor of F major? _D minor_ ✓

17   (a)   Complete in pencil your table of keys up to four sharps, writing in tonics of major and minor keys.

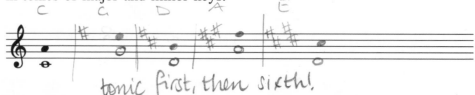

tonic first, then sixth!

(b)   Complete in pencil your table of keys up to four flats, writing in tonics of major and minor keys.

Correct any mistakes you have made before going on to **18**.

18 Once you have checked your answers in **17**, write out the series of sharp and flat keys in the bass clef, in pencil.

(a) sharp series

(b) flat series

Correct any mistakes you may have made.

**TEST 9
minor key
signatures**

1 Of what minor keys are these the key signatures?

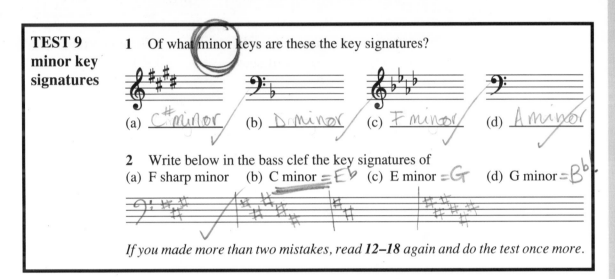

(a) _C# minor_ (b) _D minor_ (c) _F minor_ (d) _A minor_

2 Write below in the bass clef the key signatures of
(a) F sharp minor (b) C minor = Eb (c) E minor = G (d) G minor = Bb

*If you made more than two mistakes, read **12–18** again and do the test once more.*

21
(a)

(b)

(c)

(d)

22 (a) D sharp
(b) E sharp

**melodic
minor scales**

19 Melodic minor scales descend using the notes of the natural minor. When they ascend, they sharpen the <u>sixth</u> and <u>seventh</u> notes of the natural minor by a semitone.

Write out A melodic minor, descending then ascending, in crotchets.

**harmonic
minor scales**

20 Harmonic minor scales sharpen only the seventh note of the natural minor scale, but do it both when ascending and when descending.

Write out A harmonic minor, (a) ascending and (b) descending. Use the rhythms given.

(a)   (b)

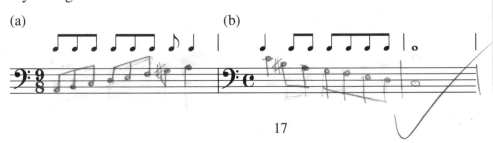

23 B sharp

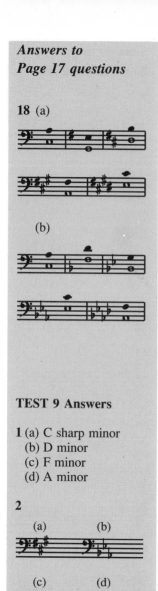

B minor

21 The key signature of B minor has two sharps, F sharp and C sharp, so the notes of B natural minor are B, C♯, D, E, F♯, G, A and top B.

The melodic minor *descends* using the same notes as B natural minor, but when it *ascends* the sixth and seventh degrees are sharpened becoming G♯ and A♯.

The harmonic minor sharpens the seventh degree to become A♯ both ascending and descending.

Write out in crotchets, using key signatures and any necessary accidentals, the scales below.

(a) B harmonic minor ascending and (b) descending.

(c) B melodic minor ascending and (d) B melodic minor descending.

F♯ minor

– melodic

22 The key of F sharp minor has three sharps, so the notes of F sharp natural minor are F♯, G♯, A, B, C♯, D, E and top F♯.

F♯ melodic minor descends like F♯ natural minor, but when it ascends the sixth and seventh degrees are sharpened.

Name (a) the 6th ___D♯___ and (b) the 7th ___E♯___ degrees of F♯ melodic minor ascending.

white note sharps

23 Look at this diagram of a keyboard. The white note, E, has no black note immediately to its right. However, the white note we usually call F is a semitone sharper than E. So this note has two names – F, and also E sharp.

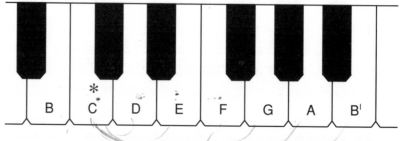

We must call the note E sharp and not F in this scale because of the rule which tells us that all the letters of the alphabet from A to G must appear once, as a sharp or a natural or a flat. (See ***Theory Time! Grade 1***, page 22 paragraph 9).

Look at the note marked * in the diagram of the keyboard above, and complete this sentence:

The note marked * can be called either C, or ___B___ sharp.

F♯ harmonic minor

24   F sharp harmonic minor sharpens the seventh note so that it becomes E sharp both ascending and descending.

Write in the accidentals needed to make the following correct.

(a) F sharp harmonic minor ascending and (b) descending:

C♯ minor

25   (a)   What sharps are in C sharp natural minor?   F, C, G, D

   (b)   Write out in crotchets C sharp natural minor ascending:

The 6th and 7th degrees of C sharp melodic minor ascending are A♯ and B♯.

B♯, like E♯ in F sharp minor, is a 'white note' sharp (*see paragraph* **24**).

Write out, using key signatures and any necessary accidentals, in the rhythms indicated, these scales.

sharp 6 + 7!

(c) C sharp melodic minor ascending and (d) descending:

sharp 7th

(e) C sharp harmonic minor ascending:

G minor

26   G minor has two flats, B♭ and E♭.

Write out the notes of the scales below in crotchets.

(a) G natural minor ascending: (b) G melodic minor descending:

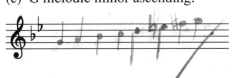   

(c) G melodic minor ascending: (d) G harmonic minor ascending:

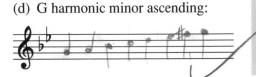

27 (a)

(b)

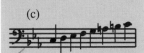

(c)

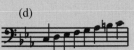

(d)

28 (a)

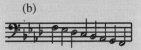

(b)

(c)

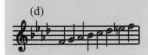

(d)

TEST 10 Answers

(a) A harmonic minor

(b) G major

(c) C♯ melodic minor

(d) B♭ major

(e) A♭ major

(f) F melodic minor

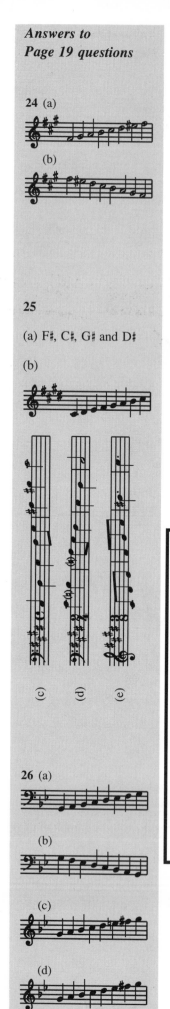

24 (a)

(b)

25

(a) F♯, C♯, G♯ and D♯

(b)

(c)   (d)   (e)

26 (a)

(b)

(c)

(d)

C minor

27 C minor has three flats, B♭, E♭ and A♭.

Write out in crotchets these scales. *Remember that sharpened flats become naturals.*

(a) C natural minor ascending:

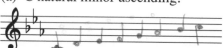

(b) C melodic minor descending:

(c) C melodic minor ascending:

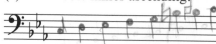

(d) C harmonic minor ascending:

F minor

28 F minor has four flats, B♭, E♭, A♭ and D♭.

Write out in minims the notes of

(a) F natural minor ascending:

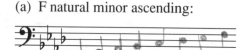

(b) F melodic minor descending:

(c) F melodic minor ascending:

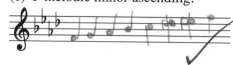

(d) F harmonic minor ascending:

TEST 10 naming scales

Name the scales used in the following. If the scale is minor, state if it is in the harmonic minor or the melodic minor.

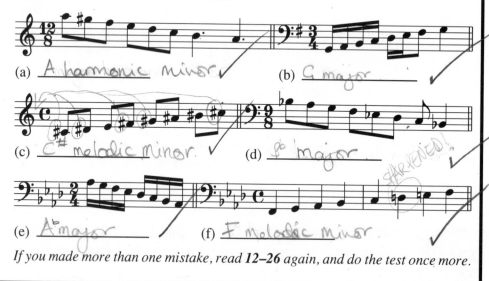

(a) A harmonic minor

(b) G major

(c) C♯ melodic minor

(d) A♭ major   *SHARPENED!*

(e) A♭ major

(f) F melodic minor

If you made more than one mistake, read 12–26 again, and do the test once more.

scales and keys

29 Notes of scales are written in order, upwards or downwards. If a piece of music uses the notes of a scale in *any* order, the piece is said to be in the **key** of that scale. Look at these examples:

Scale of G major   Music in the *key* of G major

**naming the
key of a
passage**

30 **Naming the key of a passage with a key signature.**

- (1) Decide which major and minor scale uses the key signature.
- (2) If there are no sharps or flats present except those in the key signature, the key is likely to be major.
- (3) If there are accidentals present (sharps or flats in addition to those of the key signature, or naturals), decide if they are the sixth or seventh notes of *any* form of the minor scale.

(a) What keys employ the key signature in the example? D major **X** G major/E minor!

(b) What is the name of any accidental present? D# ✓

(c) Is this accidental the sixth or seventh of a form of E minor? 7 ✓

(d) In which key is the passage? D major **X** E minor!

31 **Naming the key of a passage without a key signature.**

- Decide if the passage is in a key which uses mainly sharps or flats.

(a) Are sharps or flats mostly used here? flats.

- Arrange them as a key signature in the order in which they enter the series.
- Now follow the steps 1–3 in **30**.

(b) Which keys have this key signature? Bb major, G minor. ✓

(c) Name any accidental present in addition to the key signature. F# ✓

(d) In which key is the passage? G minor ✓ YES!

32 (a) A major

(b) D major

33 (1) C major

(2) (a) G major
(b) D major

(3) (a) B flat major
(b) F major

34 B flat major

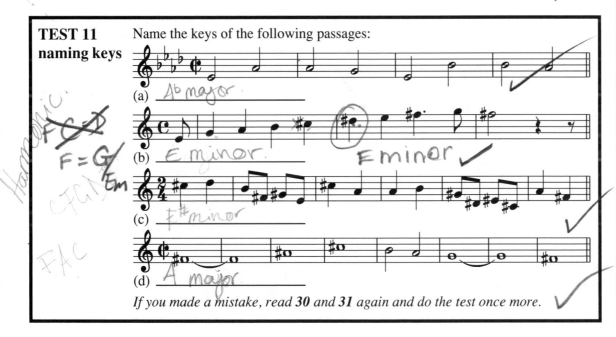

**TEST 11
naming keys** Name the keys of the following passages:

(a) Ab major

(b) E minor.   E minor ✓

(c) F# minor

(d) A major ✓

*If you made a mistake, read **30** and **31** again and do the test once more.* ✓

modulation

32 So far, we have dealt entirely with short passages of music which stay in the same key.

However, many melodies change key at least once during their course, though they almost always return later to the key in which they started.

Changing from one key to another during the course of a piece is called **modulation**.

Look at this Scottish tune, *The Bluebells of Scotland*.

30 (a) G major and
     E minor

   (b) D sharp

   (c) Yes

   (d) E minor

This starts in the key of D major. But by the beginning of bar 8, the key has changed. The two sharps of D major have been joined by G♯.

(a) What major key has F♯, C♯ and G♯? <u>A major</u>

In the last bar but one of the melody there is a G natural.

(b) In what key does the melody end? <u>D major.</u> ✓

Notice that, when the music moved for a little while from D major to A major, there was no change in the key signature.

31 (a) flats

   (b) B flat major or
       G minor

   (c) F sharp

   (d) G minor

**modulations
in major key
pieces**

33 A is the fifth note of D major, and by far the commonest type of modulation from a major key is to the key starting five notes above the original tonic.

So pieces in D major will often modulate to A major.
Pieces in C major will often modulate to G major.

(1) To what key do pieces in F major most often modulate? <u>C major</u> ✓

In what key do the passages below (a) start, and (b) end?

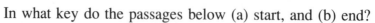

TEST 11 Answers

(a) A flat major

(b) E minor

(c) F sharp minor

(d) B minor

(2) (a) <u>G major</u>   (b) <u>D major</u> ✓

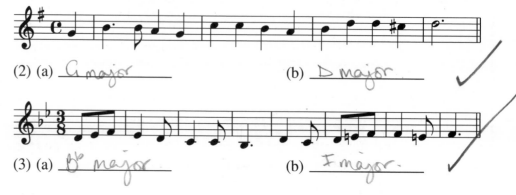

(3) (a) <u>B♭ major</u>   (b) <u>F major.</u> ✓

**modulations
in minor key
pieces**

34 Minor keys most commonly modulate to their relative majors. Modulation will be studied in more detail in later grades.

To which key is a piece in G minor most likely to modulate? <u>B♭ major</u> ✓

Answers to questions on this page are in the margin of Page 24

numbering of intervals

1 Intervals are measured by counting the number of notes from the bottom note to the top note, including the outside notes in the counting.

The intervals you need to know are the second, the third, the fourth, the fifth, the sixth, the seventh and the octave. Here they are, written melodically in the key of C major.

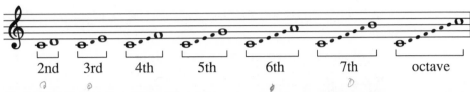

| 2nd | 3rd | 4th | 5th | 6th | 7th | octave |

quality of intervals

2 In addition to a number, each interval has a 'quality'. There are several different types of quality of interval. The ones you need to know for Grade 3 are **major**, **perfect** and **minor**. Look at the intervals in **1** again.

– major The second, third, sixth and seventh are called **major** intervals — major second, major third, major sixth and major seventh.

– perfect The fourth, fifth and octave are called **perfect** intervals.

Name these intervals, giving both number and quality. In each case, the bottom note is the keynote (= *tonic*).

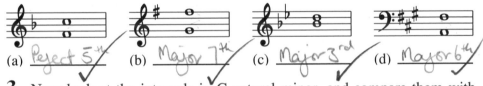

(a) _Perfect 5th_ ✓   (b) _Major 7th_ ✓   (c) _Major 3rd_ ✓   (d) _Major 6th_ ✓

intervals in natural minor scales

3 Now look at the intervals in C natural minor, and compare them with the intervals in C major in **1**.

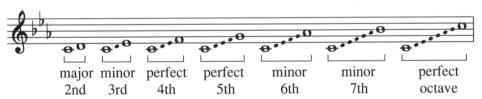

| major 2nd | minor 3rd | perfect 4th | perfect 5th | minor 6th | minor 7th | perfect octave |

Which intervals are the same in both keys?

Major 2nd, Perfect 4th, Perfect 5th, Perfect octave. ✓

The intervals between the tonic and the second, fourth, fifth and octave notes are the same in all major and natural minor keys.

– minor intervals But the intervals of the third (C–E♭), the sixth (C–A♭) and the seventh (C–B♭) are not the same in C natural minor as in C major.

In natural minor scales, the interval between the tonic and the third is called a **minor third**. It is a semitone *less* than a major third.

The interval between the tonic and the sixth is called a **minor sixth**. It is a semitone *less* than a major sixth.

The interval between the tonic and the seventh is called a **minor seventh**. It is a semitone *less* than a major seventh.

4 (a)

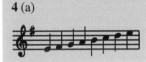

(b) No
(c) a major 6th
(d) Yes
(e) a minor 7th

TEST 12 Answers

1 (a) perfect 4th
(b) minor 3rd
(c) major 6th

2   (a)   (b)   (c)

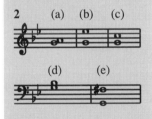

(d)   (e)

5 (a) C, E♭, G

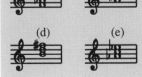

6ths and 7ths in melodic and harmonic minors

4 Remember that the sixth and seventh degrees of the natural minor scale are altered in melodic and harmonic minors. In these scales, sixths and sevenths may be either minor or major.

In Grade 3 work, the lowest note of any interval you are asked to name will always be the keynote (= *tonic*), so you may work as shown below to decide the quality of a sixth or seventh:

- write out the notes of the natural minor ascending;
- if the upper note of a sixth or a seventh is a note of the natural minor scale, the interval must be **minor**;
- if the upper note is *not* a note of the natural minor scale, the sixth or seventh must be **major**.

Look at these two intervals in E minor.

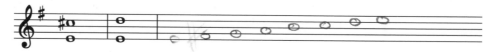

(a) Write out the notes of E natural minor ascending on the stave.

(b) Is the top note of the first interval above found in E natural minor? *no*

(c) Is the first interval a minor or a major 6th? *Major* ✓

(d) Is the top note of the second interval found in E natural minor? *yes* ✓

(e) Is the second interval a minor or a major 7th? *Minor.* ✓

---

2 (a) perfect 5th
(b) major 7th
(c) major 3rd
(d) major 6th

TEST 12 intervals

1 Give the quality and the number of each of these intervals. The lower note is the keynote.

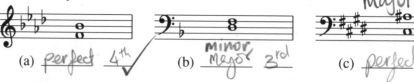

major 6th!

(a) *perfect 4th* ✓   (b) *minor Major 3rd*   (c) *perfect 5th* ✗

2 Write in upper notes to make the named intervals. The key is G minor.

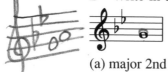 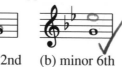 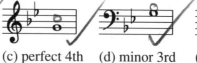

(a) major 2nd   (b) minor 6th   (c) perfect 4th   (d) minor 3rd   (e) major 7th

If you made any mistakes, re-read the section and do the test again.

---

3 major 2nd
perfect 4th
perfect 5th
perfect octave

tonic triads

5 The tonic triad of a key is a chord of three notes, the lowest of which is the keynote (= *tonic*) of the scale. The other two notes are the third and fifth degrees of the scale.

The tonic triad of C major is in the left hand margin. Its notes are C, E and G.

(a) Name the notes of the tonic triad of C minor: *C, E♭, G*

Write below, without using key signatures, the tonic triads of

(b)   F minor   (c)   A major   (d)   B minor   (e)   A♭ major

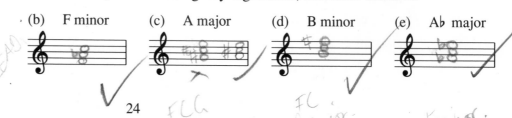

Section 5 – Phrases

Answers to questions on this page are in the margin of Page 26

Answers to questions on this page are in the margin of Page 26

1 Look at this well-known tune, a Welsh melody called *Ar hyd y Nos*.

The tune is sixteen bars long. Each bar has been numbered for you. It falls naturally into four sections of equal length, so each section is four bars long.

The sections are called **phrases**, and each has been marked with a bracket. Phrases in music can be any length, but four-bar phrases like these are most common. In most of the melodies we are dealing with in Grade 3, all phrases in the same melody will be of the same length.

2 In *Ar hyd y Nos*, the phrases all start on the first beats of bars. Often, however, phrases will start on beats *before* the first beat of the first full bar.

If a phrase does this, it is said to start on an **anacrusis**, or 'up-beat'.

Look at the next tune, which is the Scottish song *Auld Lang Syne*. It contains sixteen bars, but the first phrase starts with an anacrusis, on the quaver before the first full bar.

Notice that the last bar of *Auld Lang Syne* contains only a dotted crotchet, though the time signature is $\frac{2}{4}$. This brings us to an important rule:

- **If a tune starts with an anacrusis, the starting note and the notes of the final bar must together equal the length of a full bar.**

All the other phrases start with an upbeat on the last quaver of a bar, too. The first phrase is marked with a bracket. Put in brackets over the other phrases.

3 If a melody doesn't easily divide into four-bar phrases, see if it can be divided into eight-bar phrases or two-bar phrases instead.

4 Phrases often end with a long note. Quite often the last note is followed by a rest.

Look at *Ar hyd y Nos* in **1** again.

(a) Which phrases end with a long note? _____ 1, 2 + 3. ✓ _____

(b) Which phrases follow the long note with a rest? _____ 1 + 2. ✓ _____

Answers to Page 26 questions

5 (a) bar 4

   (b) G

   (c) bar 4

   (d) D

   (e) bar 12

   (f) Same as Phrase 1

6

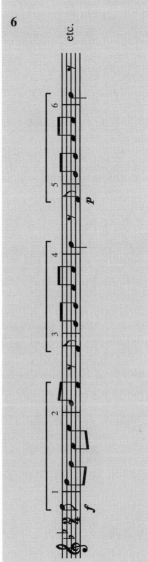

25

5 Phrases are often repeated during the course of a melody.

Look at this march, called *The British Grenadiers.*

The melody is sixteen bars long, and starts on an anacrusis.

(a) In which bar does the first phrase end? _4_ ✓

(b) What is the letter name of the last note of the first phrase? _G_ ✓

(c) In which bar does the second phrase start? _4_ 4

(d) Name the note on which Phrase 2 starts. _G_ ✗ D

(e) Phrase 3 starts on the last quaver of bar 8. In which bar does it end? _12_ ✓

(f) What do you notice about the last phrase of the piece? _repeat of phrase 1_ ✓

6 Though we have looked so far at pieces made up of four-bar phrases, it has to be repeated that phrases can be of other lengths, too.

Here is the first section of a piece by Mozart, which is made up of two-bar phrases. There is a bracket over the first phrase. Put in your own brackets over the next two phrases.

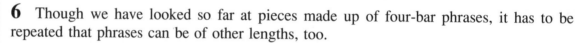

4 (a) 1, 2 and 4
  (b) 1 and 2

Section 6 – Completing four-bar rhythms

In Grade 3, you will be asked to complete four-bar rhythms.

In Grade 2, rhythms for completion always started on the first beat of the bar, but in Grade 3 the rhythms may start with an anacrusis.

In Grade 2 you were always given the opening of the rhythm to continue. In Grade 3 you may be asked to write the beginning yourself, but to include a given rhythmic figure in the course of the four-bar phrase.

Revise the section about writing rhythms in ***Theory Time! Grade 2***.

1 To continue a rhythm which starts with a given opening, like this:

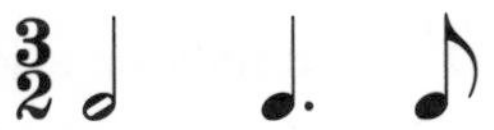

First, draw the framework of the four bars, and pencil over the top the main beats.

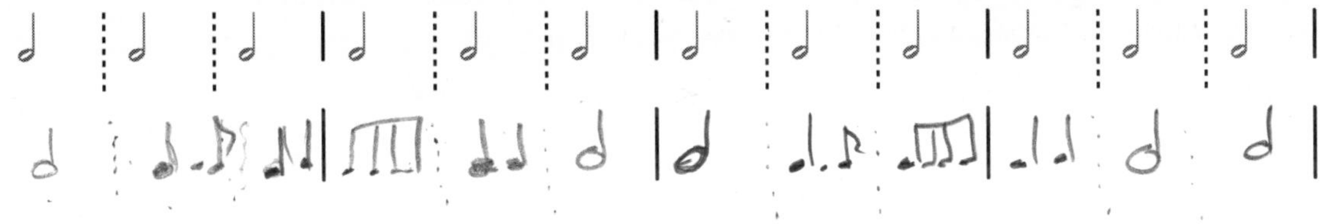

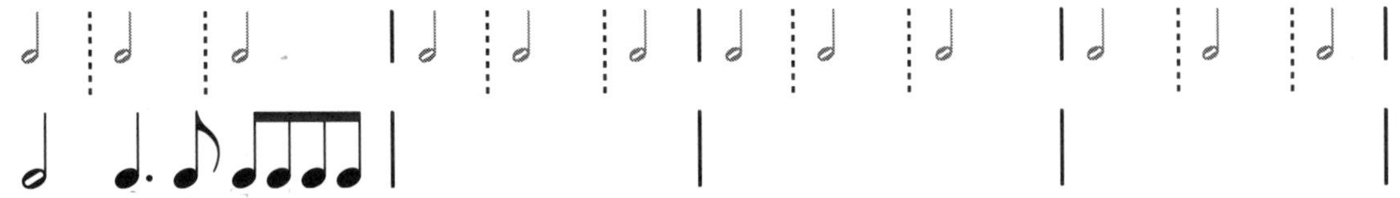

make up rhythms that fit 3/2

Complete the first bar, using a fairly simple rhythm.

Add a second bar which balances the first.

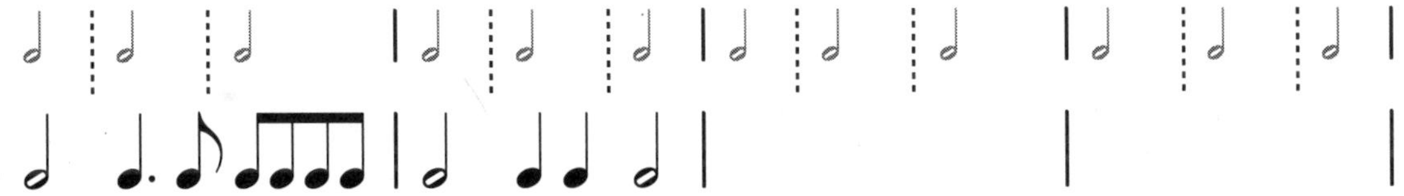

Now write a third that can be the same, or nearly the same, as the first.

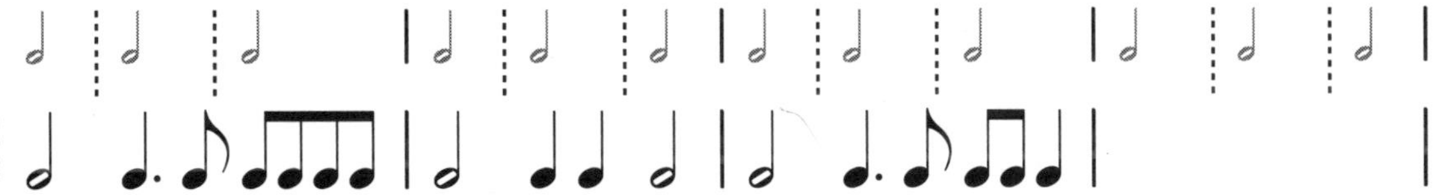

Write a final bar in which the last note should not be shorter than a beat.

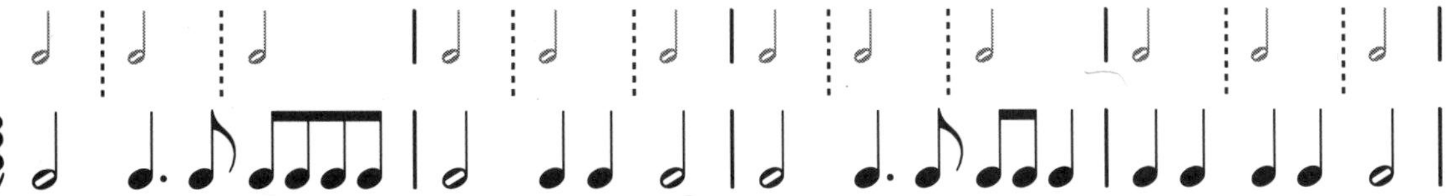

Answers to Page 28 questions

2 (a) 2
(b) 2
(c) 1⅔

2 If you are asked to write a rhythm which starts with an anacrusis, the fourth bar will not have a full number of beats. Remember the rule, that the anacrusis and the last bar of a phrase **together** must equal a complete bar.

Write in the spaces the number of beats that there will be in the final bars of phrases which start as follows:

(a) ____2____   (b) ____2____   (c) ____5____

3 You may be asked to continue a rhythm for which no opening is given, but in which you are asked to include a rhythmic idea, for example:

Draw the framework of the four bars, with the main beats pencilled over the top. Write a simple opening: include the given rhythm in the first bar, if possible.

Now add bars 3 and 4 just as you were shown in **1** above.

Here are some practice exercises for you.

Complete these four-bar rhythms, the openings of which are given:

(a) $\frac{3}{8}$

(b) $\frac{12}{8}$

(c) $\frac{4}{4}$

(d) Write a four-bar rhythm including this rhythmic figure: $\frac{2}{2}$

(e) Write a four-bar rhythm including this rhythmic figure: $\frac{3}{4}$

Section 7 – Terms and Signs

Answers to questions on this page are in the margin of Page 30

Answers to Page 30 questions

A list of the musical terms and signs you must know for Grade 3 is printed on Pages 31 and 32. Many of the terms are sufficiently explained by their English translations.

tempo

1 There are only a few new terms describing tempo. *Adagietto* means less slow than *adagio*. Compare it with *allegretto*, which means less fast than *allegro*.

Tempo comodo means at a convenient, or comfortable speed. This isn't a very exact direction, but it does suggest the choice of a tempo which can be maintained without strain.

Tempo rubato is a very important direction. It means that the performer should vary the pulse, getting faster in some places and slower in others.

A tempo means 'in time'. It is often used after directions like *rallentando* and *accelerando* to tell the performer to return to the original tempo of the piece.

What Italian term on your list is similar in meaning to *stringendo*?

_____

manner of performance

2 Most of the terms which are new for this grade are about the manner of performance. They have to be memorised, but you can help yourself in this work by making use of your knowledge of English.

For example, *ad libitum* means freely, or 'as you wish'. Compare it with being 'at liberty'.

Here are two lists of words, one Italian and one English. Choose a word from the English list, and write it in the space after the Italian word which you think may have a similar meaning.

tranquil (= calm)
martial
agitated
marked
rhythmic
force
resolute
first
simple
delicate
second
decisive
animated (= lively)
energetic

(a) *agitato* _agitated_ ✓
(b) *animato* _animated_ ✓
(c) *deciso* _decisive_ ✓
(d) *delicato* _delicate_ ✓
(e) *energico* _energetic_ ✓
(f) *forza* _force_ ✓
(g) *marcato* _Marked_ ✓
(h) *marziale* _martial_ ✓
(i) *prima* (as in 'primary') _First_ ✓
(j) *risoluto* _resolute_ ✓
(k) *ritmico* _rhythmic_ ✓
(l) *secondo* _Second_ ✓
(m) *semplice* _simple_ ✓
(n) *tranquillo* _tranquil_ ✓

1 (a) F major
   (b) C major

2 (a) with love
   (b) a little faster than a walking pace (or *andante*)
   (c) held back a little
   (d) return to the original speed (literally, 'in time')

3 (a) F
   (b) four times

4 pause

5 the rhythms are the same

6   **7**

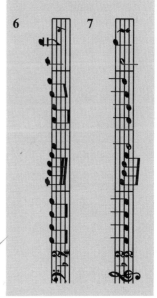

Coda – fitting your knowledge together

Answers to questions on this page are in the margin of Page 29

Now that you have come to the end of this book, you will be able to understand more about the pieces of music you play, sing, or compose yourself.

See if you can answer the questions about this piece of music.

*Answers to
Page 29 questions*

1   *accelerando*

1   In what key is the music:
    (a)   in bar 1? F major   ✓
    (b)   in bar 10? C major   ✓

2   What are the meanings of the following terms?
    (a)   *con amore* (bar 1) With love.
    (b)   **andantino** (bar 1) A little faster than andante ✓
    (c)   *poco ritenuto* (bar 11) held back a little ✓
    (d)   a tempo (bar 13) return to the original speed

2 (a) agitated

  (b) animated (= lively)

  (c) decisive

  (d) delicate

  (e) energetic

  (f) force

  (g) marked

  (h) martial

  (i) first

  (j) resolute

  (k) rhythmic

  (l) second

  (m) simple

  (n) tranquil

3   (a)   What is the letter name of the highest note? F ✓
    (b)   How many times does it occur? 4

4   What is the meaning of the ⌢ sign in bar 10? Pause ✓

5   Compare the rhythm of bars 1–2 with 5–6: The same. ✓

6   This song is written here in the treble clef. Transpose bars 1–4 down an octave, writing the notes in the bass clef. Be careful to put in the time signature and key signature, and the new clef.

7   Re-write bars 1–4 in notes twice as long, in $\frac{2}{2}$ time. The first note is written for you.

Musical Terms & Signs

New terms for Grade 3 are <u>underlined</u>

Tempo

a tempo	in time (*tempo* means time)
<u>*adagietto*</u>	slow, but less slow than *adagio*
adagio	slow, leisurely
allegro	fairly fast
allegretto	fairly fast, but less fast than *allegro*
andante	at a moderate walking pace
andantino	a little faster than *andante*
grave	very slow and solemn
larghetto	fairly slow
largo	slow and dignified, broad
lento	slow
moderato	at a moderate speed
presto	fast
<u>*tempo comodo*</u>	at a comfortable speed
vivace, vivo	fast and lively

Changes to Tempo

accelerando	getting faster gradually
allargando	broadening – slower
rallentando (rall.)	getting slower gradually
ritardando (rit.) (or *ritard.*)	getting slower gradually
ritenuto (rit.)	holding back
<u>*rubato*</u> <u>*tempo rubato*</u>	with some freedom in time
<u>*stringendo*</u>	getting faster gradually
<u>*tenuto (ten.)*</u>	held

Dynamics

*forte (**f**)*	loud
*forte piano (**fp**)*	loud, then immediately soft
*fortissimo (**ff**)*	very loud
*mezzo forte (**mf**)*	moderately loud
*piano (**p**)*	quiet
*pianissimo (**pp**)*	very quiet
*mezzo piano (**mp**)*	moderately quiet

Changes to Dynamics

crescendo (cresc.)	gradually getting louder
decrescendo	gradually getting quieter
diminuendo (dim.)	gradually getting quieter
sforzato, sforzando	accented loudly (*sf* or *sfz*)

Manner of Performance

<u>*ad libitum*</u>	freely, as you wish
<u>*agitato*</u>	agitated
<u>*amore, con amore*</u>	with love
<u>*animato*</u>	animated and lively
<u>*brio, con*</u>	with vigour
cantabile	in a singing style
<u>*deciso, con deciso*</u>	with decision
<u>*delicato, con delicato*</u>	with delicacy
dolce	sweetly
<u>*energico, con*</u>	with energy
espressivo	expressively
<u>*forza, con forza*</u>	with force
giocoso	playful
grazioso	graceful
<u>*largamente*</u>	broadly
legato	smoothly
leggiero	lightly
maestoso	majestic
marcato	marked
<u>*marziale*</u>	in a martial style
mesto	sad
moto, mosso	movement
<u>*pesante*</u>	heavy
<u>*risoluto, con*</u>	with determination
ritmico	rhythmically
<u>*scherzando, scherzoso*</u>	playful, joking
<u>*semplice*</u>	simple, uncomplicated
sostenuto	sustained
staccato	sharp, detached
tranquillo	tranquil, calm
<u>*triste, tristamente*</u>	sad, sorrowful

Other

da capo (D.C.)	(repeat) from the beginning
dal segno (D.S.)	(repeat) from the sign
fine	end
<u>*prima volta*</u>	first time
<u>*seconda volta*</u>	second time

Qualifying words

Molto in front of a word means 'very' or 'much'. For example, *molto allegro* means 'very fast'.
Meno means 'less'. *Più* means 'more'. *Senza* means 'without'. *Con* means 'with'. *E* or *ed* means 'and'.
Non means 'not'. *Troppo* means 'too much'.
Poco in front of a word means 'little', or 'slightly'. For example, *poco crescendo* means 'getting slightly louder'.
Assai means 'very'. *Simile* means 'in the same way'. *Al* or *alla* means 'in the manner of'. *Ma* means 'but'.
<u>*Sempre*</u> means 'always'. <u>*Subito*</u> means 'immediately'. <u>*Tanto*</u> means 'so much'.

Signs used in Music

is often used for *crescendo*.

is often used for *diminuendo*.

A dot over or under a note means that the note is to be played staccato:

If staccato notes are slurred, they should be played semi-staccato – not as short as ordinary staccato notes.

A triangle means a very sharp staccato.

A > sign over or under a note means that the note must be accented. The sign ∧ means an even stronger accent:

The sign ∩ over or under a note means that the performer should pause on the note:

MM is short for Maelzel's Metronome. The performer is to set the metronome to the number which follows. If the direction is, for example, MM ♩ = 60, it means that there should be sixty crotchet beats to the minute.

8va - - - - - - - - - - - - ⌐ over a group of notes means that you must play the marked note an octave higher. The sign *8va* - - - - - - - ⌐ written under notes means that the notes must be played an octave lower.

A slur over or under a group of notes means that the notes should be played *legato* – in other words, joined together. Don't confuse this sign with the tie, which links together two notes of the same pitch.

The marks at the end mean that you must go back to the first marks, and repeat the music between the marks.

Printed by
Halstan & Co. Ltd., Amersham, Bucks. England

12/04 (53388)